W9-AAE-251

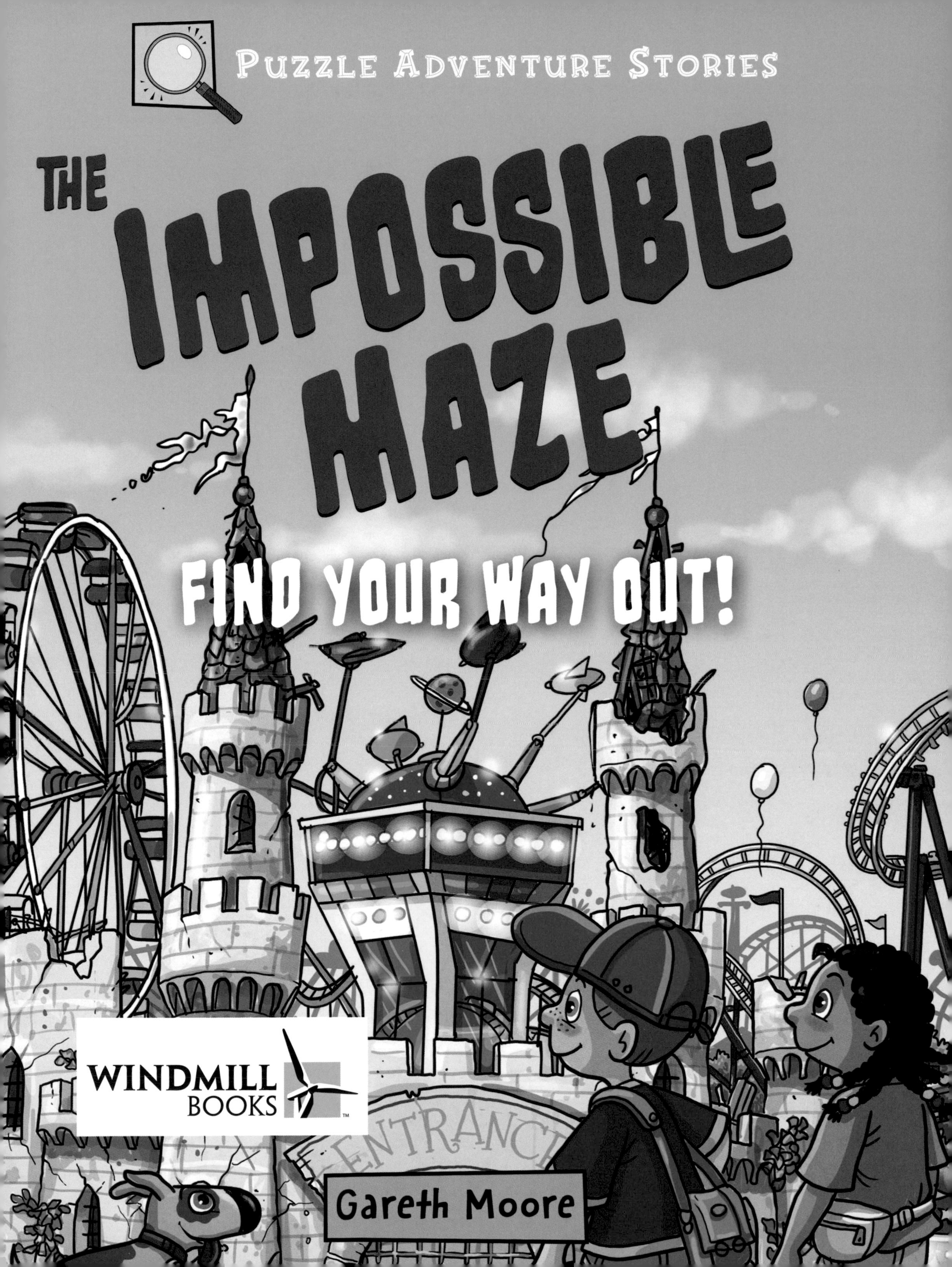
PUZZLE ADVENTURE STORIES
THE IMPOSSIBLE MAZE
FIND YOUR WAY OUT!
WINDMILL BOOKS
ENTRANCE
Gareth Moore

Published in 2019 by **Windmill Books**, an imprint of Rosen Publishing
29 East 21st Street, New York, NY 10010

Written by Gareth Moore
Illustrated by Moreno Chiacchiera
Designed by Paul Oakley, with Emma Randall
Edited by Frances Evans, with Julia Adams

Cataloging-in-Publication Data

Names: Moore, Gareth.
Title: The impossible maze / Gareth Moore.
Description: New York : Windmill Books, 2019. | Series: Puzzle adventure stories
Identifiers: LCCN ISBN 9781499484588 (pbk.) | ISBN 9781508196297 (library bound) | ISBN 9781508195443 (6 pack)
Subjects: LCSH: Amusement parks--Juvenile fiction. | Puzzles--Juvenile fiction.
Classification: LCC PZ7.M5565 Im 2019 | DDC [E]--dc23

Manufactured in the United States of America

CPSIA Compliance Information: Batch #BS18WM: For Further Information contact Rosen Publishing, New York, New York at 1-800-237-9932

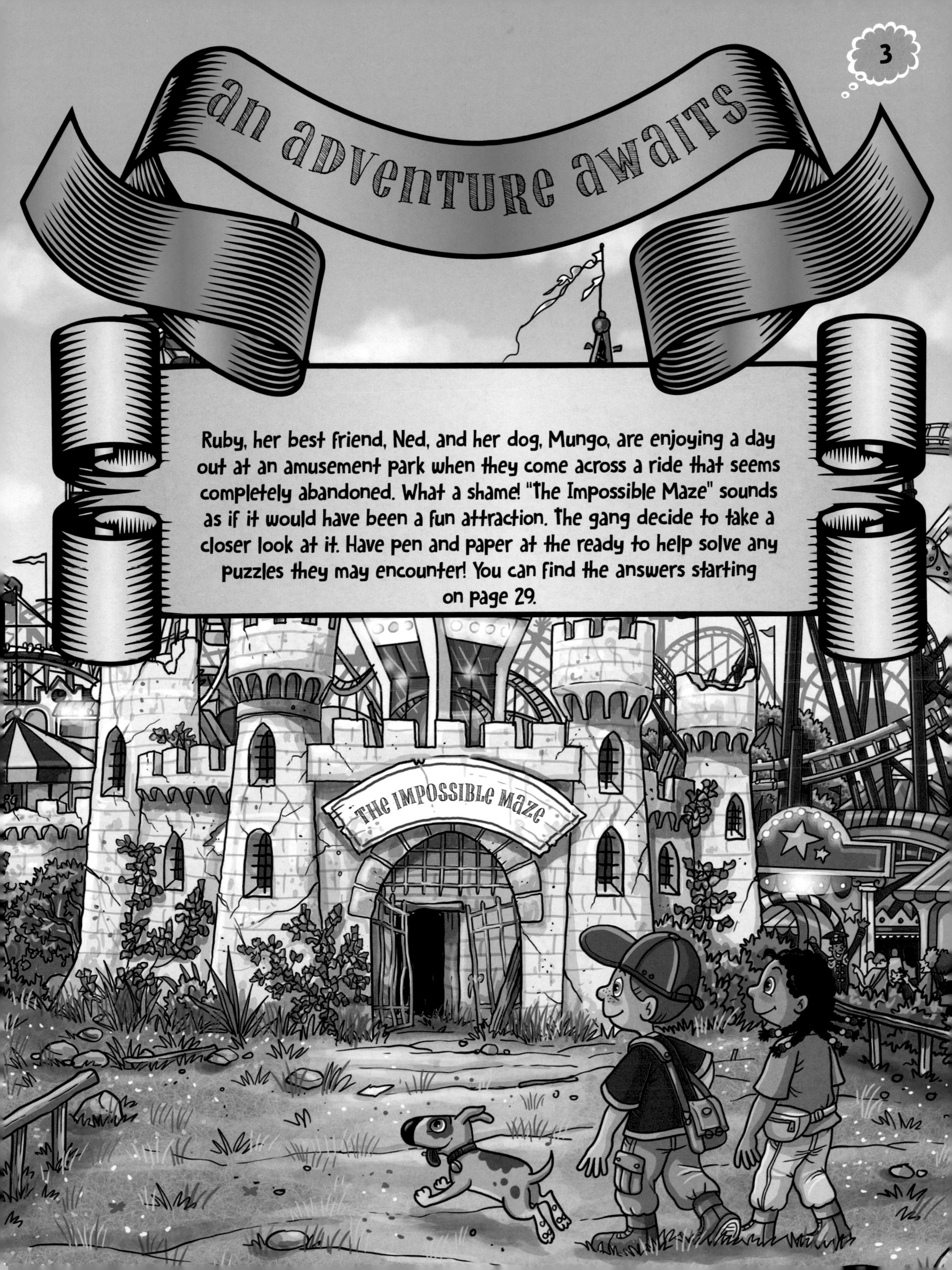
an adventure awaits
Ruby, her best friend, Ned, and her dog, Mungo, are enjoying a day out at an amusement park when they come across a ride that seems completely abandoned. What a shame! "The Impossible Maze" sounds as if it would have been a fun attraction. The gang decide to take a closer look at it. Have pen and paper at the ready to help solve any puzzles they may encounter! You can find the answers starting on page 29.
THE IMPOSSIBLE MAZE

The abandoned Ride
Ruby, Ned, and Mungo take a closer look at the attraction. It looks very old, as if it hasn't been used for a long time. Ruby spots a strange message on the wall. Can you tell what it says?
THE IMPOSSIBLE MAZE
Do you think someone's in there?
Please help us! Don't use the front door. Find another way in!

Roller Coasters

Ruby and Ned want to investigate, but they don't want to use the front door! They decide to look for another way in. There are three roller coasters nearby, which might help. Which one should they ride to get a better view of the Impossible Maze? Trace the routes with your finger to find out.

a Closer Look

The roller coaster travels around and around the theme park until it passes by the roof of the Impossible Maze. Can you spot a way for them to get into the building via the roof?

Climbing the Wall

After their ride, the children hurry back to the Impossible Maze. They walk around to the side of the building. Can you find a route to the roof that avoids broken ladders and the cat?

The Trapdoor

Ruby and Ned reach the roof and find the trapdoor they saw from the roller coaster. It is locked with a padlock, though. Can you find a hidden key that they can use to open it?

Message Board

Ruby spots a sign that might have useful information on it. Can you figure out what it says? Write the message down on your piece of paper.

- ENEMIES
- OPEN
- THE
- GOBLINS
- RIDE
- FRIENDLY
- UNICORNS
- ARE
- IS

Too Many Keys

Ned has found the key ring with four different keys on it. He kneels by the trapdoor to unlock it.

Which key should Ned use to open the trapdoor?

another Lock

Luckily, Ruby spots another key, and this one works. She opens the padlock, but instead of releasing the trapdoor, the lock springs open to reveal three number dials, plus a sheet of instructions that they unfold and read. What is the three-digit code they need to open the padlock?

To open
the padlock,
add the number of days
in a leap year to
the number of keys
on the keyring.

Goblin alert!

With the padlock finally unlocked, Ruby and Ned open the trapdoor, and climb down into the room below. Standing in the middle is a strange creature, like a goblin from a fairy tale. The fairground ride really is magic! The strange creature greets them with a rhyme.

Which of these two mazes can be solved? The other is impossible! Trace the route with your finger.

Mirror Mirror

The goblin—whose name is Garibaldi—nods as the children pick the correct maze. He tells them he needs to give them one more test before they can continue, then he suddenly darts off. The children follow him, to discover him standing in front of some mirrors.

Which of the magical reflections exactly matches Garibaldi?

The Goblin's Tale

Garibaldi tells Ned and Ruby his tale. The Impossible Maze was once the most wonderful fairground ride in the world, until it was cursed by an evil wizard. Now all the people inside have been turned into goblins! "We may look a little weird, but we're not creatures to be feared."

Before they go any farther, the children will need some supplies! Each box contains an object that does not appear in the other box. Which two objects are they?

Help from you
I now beseech.
Which items are
unique to each?

Enter the Impossible Maze

Ruby and Ned take the two unique items from the boxes, and Garibaldi leads them to a row of doors. He tells them that one will allow them to continue their journey into the Impossible Maze. Which door should they take?

Stairs

Using Garibaldi's clue, they open the correct door and walk through. Ruby and Ned then discover two staircases leading down into the maze. Which one should they take?

Shadows

They descend the staircase, and enter a dimly lit room. The goblin tells them they will need one other vital piece of equipment.

What item should Ned and Ruby pick?

It's something that was in the equipment crate— Remember or darkness will be your fate!

Powering Up

Ruby and Ned pick the flashlight but it is missing its batteries. It takes two, and needs batteries that add up to eleven volts in total. Can you figure out which two batteries they should use?

Too Many Doors

They turn on the flashlight, and finally light up the entire room. Wow! The room is full of doors—and lots of goblins! But which way to go? Their goblin guide gives them a clue:

Which door does not have a goblin pointing at it?

We point at doors but none are true. So, which of these should you go through?

Don't Turn Right!

Behind the correct door, they find a strange room with a winding path across it. The goblin tells them that they must make their way along the path to the other side of the room, but they must not turn right. What path should they take? Trace it with your finger.

Locked In!

They find their way into what appears to be a goblin treasure room. But as soon as they step in, the doors slam shut, trapping them on the inside and Garibaldi on the outside. Can you find a key somewhere in the room that they might be able to use to unlock the doors?

another exit
Ned tries to use the key that they found, but it snaps in half in the lock. Now they can't unlock the doors! Can you find another way for them to get out of the room?
I shall sniff it out!

Through the Ducts

Ruby, Ned, and Mungo enter the hidden air ducts within the building. They need to find a route to another room. Can you help them find their way? Trace the pathway with your finger.

Tall Tails
Ruby and Ned push open the grille and emerge into a new room. They are surprised to find a group of unicorns ... and even more surprised to hear one speak! "We are trapped in here. To lift the curse, you must set us free."
Are they real?!
Please help us!
Only one of these unicorns is a true rainbow-tailed unicorn, however. Can you figure out which one it is?

Potion Picking

"How can we set you free?" asks Ned. The unicorn who first spoke is called Star Sparkle. She tells them they will need to cast a spell. "Figure out the name of the spell and the ingredients, then take them to the big machine."

A Game of Gems

Ruby and Ned have discovered the spell name, but now they need to find out which magic ingredients they need. The list is in a book locked inside one of these chests. Star Sparkle tells them to open the chest of the highest value.

To the Basement

Star Sparkle whinnies with excitement. Ruby and Ned now have everything they need! She stamps her hooves on the floor, revealing a hidden opening that leads down a flight of stairs. Ruby, Ned, and Mungo need to go down the stairs, but not all of the stairs can take their weight. Which ones should they step over?

A Magical Number

At the bottom of the stairs, Ruby and Ned meet some more goblins. "Help us cast this spell and then we will be human again!" Can they figure out how to move the arrows on the dials, so together the numbers add up to 50?

25
20

18
15

14
12

Just turn the hands
upon the dials,
for unicorn and
goblin smiles!

Mixed-up Ingredients

Now that the magic machine is working, Ned and Ruby just need to put the spell ingredients into it and say the magic words! Can you find all the ingredients that were listed in the book in the unicorns' chest?

The Greatest Ride in the World
Ruby and Ned cast their magical spell, and in the blink of an eye they are standing back outside the fairground ride, now restored to its former glory. Look: Garibaldi is human again, and wearing a fancy uniform! There's just one message they spot that reminds them of their adventure.
TIP: Look at page 8!

Answers

Page 4 The message on the wall says "Please help us! Don't use the front door. Find another way in!"

Page 5

Page 6

Page 7

Page 8 (Top)

Page 8 (Bottom)
The secret message says:
THE GOBLINS ARE FRIENDLY.

Page 9 None of these keys will open the padlock.

Page 10 The code to open the padlock is 370.
Number of days in a leap year = 366
Number of keys on the keyring = 4
366 + 4 = 370

Page 11

Page 12

Page 13

Page 14 (Top) They need to go through the purple door.

Page 14 (Bottom) They need to use the right-hand staircase.

Page 15 They pick the flashlight, on the far left.

Page 16 They need to pick the batteries marked 7V and 4V.

Page 17

Page 18

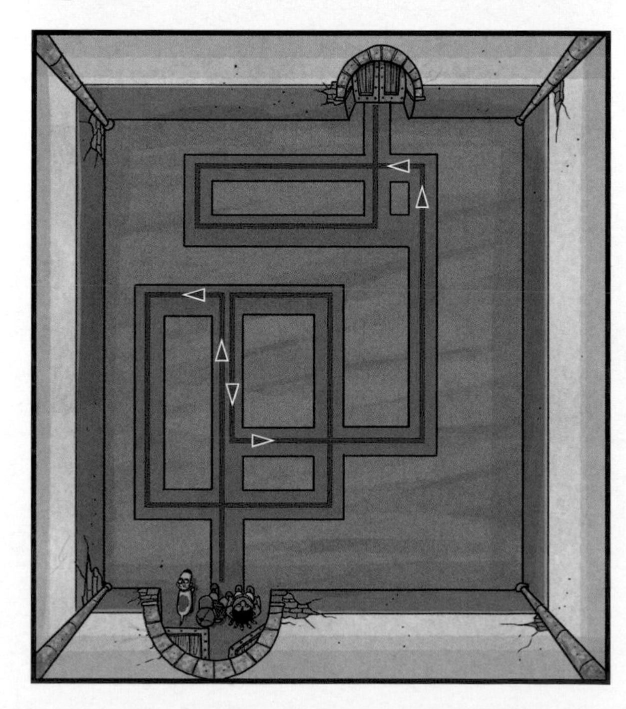

Page 19

Page 20 They can use the air duct hidden behind the painting.

Page 21

Page 22

Page 23 The name of the spell is Hocus Pocus. There are seven stars on the unicorn's back, which is an odd number. The total number of points on the stars is 7 x 5 = 35. That is not a multiple of 6.

Page 24 The correct chest is A
A is 2 + 4 + 4 + 5 = 15
B is 2 + 2 + 3 + 4 = 11
C is 2 + 3 + 4 + 5 = 14
D is 2 + 3 + 4 + 5 = 14

Page 25 The children can use these steps.
2 = prime number
3 = prime number and multiple of 3
5 = prime number
6 = multiple of 3
7 = prime number
9 = multiple of 3
They should step over 1, 4, 8, and 10.

Page 26 The numbers that add up to 50 are 20, 18, and 12.

Page 27

Page 28 The sign reads
THE RIDE IS OPEN

Glossary

beseech To plead with someone; to ask them urgently.

fate A force, higher being, or power that some people believe decides what will happen to you in the future.

prime number A number that can only be divided by itself and 1.

rung A step on a ladder.

unique One-of-a-kind.

volt A unit used to measure electricity.

Further Information

Books:

Moore, Gareth. *Brain Games for Clever Kids.* London, UK: Buster Books, 2014.

Regan, Lisa. *The Big Book of Riddles.* London, UK: Arcturus, 2014.

Usborne Publishing. *100 Logic Puzzles.* London, UK: Usborne Publishing, 2015.

Websites

For web resources related to the subject of this book, go to:
www.windmillbooks.com/weblinks
and select this book's title.

Index